THE SESAME STREET SONGBOOK

THE SESAME STREET SONGBOOK

Featuring Songs By

Jeff Moss   Joe Raposo

Christopher Cerf   Tony Geiss
Stephen Lawrence   Sam Pottle

And Other Sesame Street Songwriters

Illustrations by David Prebenna

Arrangements by Andy Brick, Porter Blackburn,
Sy Oliver and Denes Agay

Special Edition Printed For Hal Leonard Publishing Corp.

Macmillan Publishing Company   New York
Maxwell Macmillan Canada   Toronto
Maxwell Macmillan International
New York   Oxford   Singapore   Sydney

Macmillan Publishing Company
866 Third Avenue
New York, NY 10022

Maxwell Macmillan Canada, Inc.
1200 Eglinton Avenue East
Suite 200
Don Mills, Ontario M3C 3N1

Macmillan Publishing Company is part of the
Maxwell Communication Group of Companies.

Library of Congress Cataloging-in-Publication Data
Sesame Street songbook : 64 favorite songs from Sesame Street/
featuring songs by Christopher Cerf, Jeffrey Moss, and Joe Raposo;
musical arrangements by Andy Brick
1 score.
For voice and piano; includes chord symbols.
Summary: Easy arrangements for voice, piano, and guitar of some
sixty-four popular songs from the television show "Sesame Street."
ISBN 0-02-525141-4
1. Children's songs. [1. Songs.] I. Cerf, Christopher.
II. Moss, Jeffrey. III. Raposo, Joe. IV. Brick, Andy. V. Sesame Street (Television Program)
M1977.S4847 1992   92-6602   CIP   AC M

Special thanks to Chris Cerf, Danny Epstein, Ruth Luwisch and Jeff Moss.

Book design by Janet Tingey

Macmillan books are available at special discounts
for bulk purchases for sales promotions, premiums, fund-raising, or educational use.
For details, contact:
Special Sales Director
Macmillan Publishing Company
866 Third Avenue
New York, NY 10022

10 9 8 7 6 5 4 3 2 1

Printed in the United States of America

Foreword

by Joan Ganz Cooney

One of the happiest moments of my life occurred not very long ago, in 1989, when I was invited back to receive an award at graduation ceremonies at my alma mater, the University of Arizona. The graduating class responded to the award citation by singing the "Sesame Street Theme"—the very first song you'll find in this book. I was thrilled to hear that song from so many young people who'd started their education by watching *Sesame Street,* and who'd gone on to be successful in school.

I hope that *The Sesame Street Songbook* will give you and your family many happy moments as well. The *Songbook* spans twenty-three years of the show's music, offering a choice sampling of the hundreds of wonderful songs that have been written for the series. We made sure to include classics like "Rubber Duckie," "Bein' Green," and "People in Your Neighborhood," as well as contemporary hits for today's preschoolers and their parents, like "We Are all Earthlings," "Opposite Song," and "Born to Add," inspired by Bruce Springsteen.

Music and songs have always been essential to *Sesame Street.* When we at Children's Television Workshop set out to create the series, we felt that the right music would help give *Sesame Street* personality and charm—indeed its own sound. Just as important, songs could help make learning fun.

We had a hunch that songs would be wonderfully suited to educational television. They are a terrific means for *Sesame Street* to achieve its goal: to help children learn cognitive skills such as recognizing letters and numbers, and emotional skills such as developing self-esteem and cooperating with others. "C Is for Cookie," for example, is an early favorite that introduces children to a letter's sound. Another classic, "Five People in My Family," covers both counting and family relationships. "It Sure Is Hot," a rollicking tune peppered with Spanish words, helps youngsters appreciate people from diverse backgrounds.

The songs of *Sesame Street* also appeal to children's inherent love of music. Singing, dancing, and keeping time are among the very first ways that children learn to express themselves. Our talented composers and lyricists have tried to give young singers a sense of music's great cultural and ethnic variety. They have drawn upon many musical styles and traditions, from grand opera to calypso to rock and roll, from boogie-woogie to salsa to indigenous African rhythms.

The more than sixty songs presented here include the very popular "Keep Christmas With You," from our holiday special, *Christmas Eve on Sesame Street.* You'll find slow, lyrical ballads like "I Don't Want to Live on the Moon," interactive songs like "Pat Pat Patty Pat" which invites you to pat your tummy and wiggle your toes while you sing along, and songs to dance to, like "Fuzzy and Blue," written in soft-shoe style.

If you ask your child to sing you a favorite song, chances are you'll hear something from this songbook. You most certainly will after you and your family start enjoying—and learning from—these songs. I believe that they represent the best of *Sesame Street.*

A final word: We owe many of these fine compositions to the late Joe Raposo, *Sesame Street*'s first musical director. Special thanks to Jeff Moss who kindly helped with the arrangement of these songs for intermediate-level play.

Introduction

by Jeff Moss

Late in 1969, as *Sesame Street* was preparing to go on the air for the first time, Joe Raposo and I had a brief meeting. I had been hired to write scripts for the show, and as its musical director, Joe's primary job was to compose the show's theme song and to help choose records that would be the show's major source of music. But, that day, he had discovered that there was no simple way for public television to get permission to use songs from records.

So . . .

"Look, it's simple!" Joe said to me with his inimitable enthusiasm. "I write songs, and I know you write songs. We both write words, we both write music. We can do it better, faster, and cheaper than records. What do you say?"

Later that week, part of my script assignment included writing a piece designed to teach the number five, and I used the opportunity to write my first song for *Sesame Street*. It was a soft-shoe number sung by a family of Anything Muppets and it was called "Five People In My Family." I've been writing songs for *Sesame Street* ever since.

The early days remain special and vivid in my memory. I remember Joe on a winter's day during the first season of the show, walking down the hall from office to office with his new hand-held cassette recorder, a recent invention in 1970. He was playing, for anyone who would listen, his recording of the two songs he and I had written that week—"Bein' Green" (his) and "Rubber Duckie" (mine). I also remember the recording session for the first *Sesame Street* record album. Working in an old studio that had once been a church, we started recording at ten in the morning and finished at ten the following morning, with Jim Henson as Kermit the Frog recording "Bein' Green" at about three A.M. I remember later that same year we went to Boston and heard our music played by the Boston Pops Orchestra in Symphony Hall. At one point all the members of the orchestra were using rubber ducks as musical instruments, squeezing them in time to the music. Writing songs for *Sesame Street* has always included a bit of the unexpected.

Through the years, as new songwriters like Chris Cerf, Sam Pottle, Tony Geiss, and Steve Lawrence have joined the *Sesame Street* team, the process of writing songs has remained basically the same as it was in the early days. Almost every song that is created for *Sesame Street* is written to teach one of the shows specific educational subjects. Writing lyrics for *Sesame Street* songs requires a working knowledge of a wide curriculum that has been built and shaped through the years by educational experts. A writer may be called on to cover any number of subjects; for example, there are songs in this book that were written to help teach subjects as diverse as ecology ("We Are All Earthlings"), addition ("Born to Add"), self-esteem ("Frogs in the Glen"), health ("Captain Vegetable"), and the letter C ("C Is for Cookie"). It may be interesting to note that the musical styles of *Sesame Street* are as diverse as the show's educational subjects. The music for the five songs just mentioned includes a soft-rock ballad, hard rock, a waltz, a march, and what might be best described as an anthem.

There is one more thing about writing *Sesame Street* songs that has remained the same through the years. From the first days of the show through to today, as we begin work on the twenty-fourth season, there has never been any "talking down" to our audience. We have always tried to make sure that the songs deal with experiences and emotions that kids can understand, but we have also always aimed to write songs that we hope both kids and adults will enjoy and remember. Fortunately, although it is now hundreds of songs later, it still seems there are plenty of songs left to write.

Sesame Street Theme

Words by Bruce Hart, Jon Stone, and Joe Raposo
Music by Joe Raposo

Steady Rock March

Sun - ny day sweep - in' the clouds a - way.
Come and play! Eve - ry - thing's A - O - K.

On my way to where the air is sweet. Can you
Friend - ly neigh - bors there, that's where we meet. Can you

Bein' Green

Words and music by Joe Raposo

Rubber Duckie

Words and music by Jeff Moss

is for Cookie

Words and music by Joe Raposo

People In Your Neighborhood

Words and music by Jeff Moss

Soft Shoe

Oh, ___ who ___ are the peo-ple in your
(Oh, the) post-man is a per-son in your

neigh - bor - hood, in your neigh - bor - hood, in your
neigh - bor - hood, in your neigh - bor - hood, in your

Sing

Words and music by Joe Raposo

I Love Trash

Words and music by Jeff Moss

Brightly

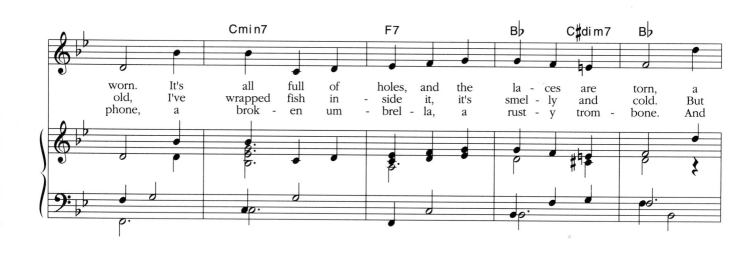

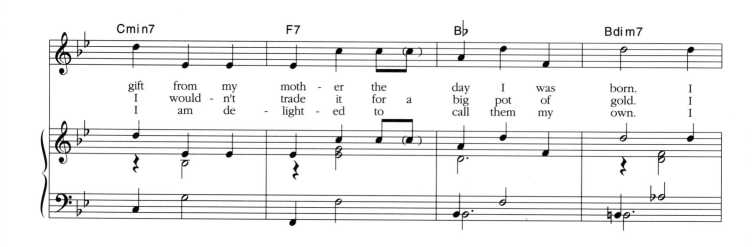

ABC - DEF - GHI

Words by Joe Raposo and Jon Stone
Music by Joe Raposo

March

AB - C - DEF - GHI - J - KL - M - NOP - QR - STUV - WX - YZ_____ It's the

most re - mar - ka - ble word I've ev - er seen.

I Don't Want to Live on the Moon

Words and music by Jeff Moss

I DON'T WANT TO LIVE ON THE MOON 29

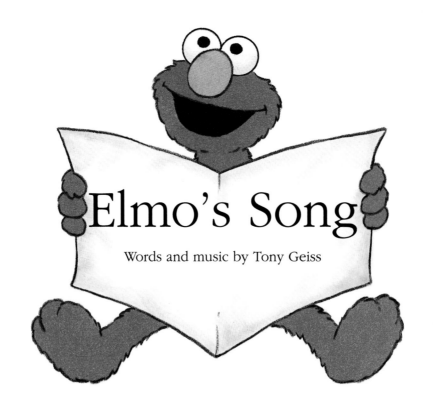

Elmo's Song

Words and music by Tony Geiss

Octopus Blues

Words and music
by Jeff Moss

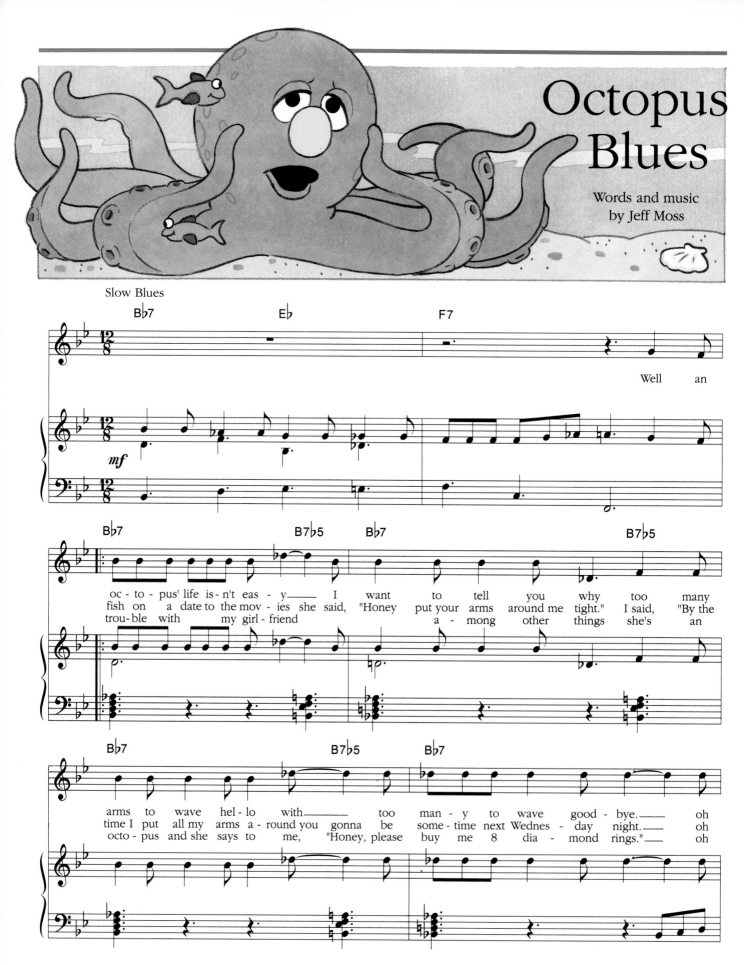

Slow Blues

oc - to - pus' life is - n't eas - y____ I want to tell you why too many
fish on a date to the mov - ies she said, "Hon-ey put your arms around me tight." I said, "By the
trou-ble with my girl - friend a - mong other things she's an

arms to wave hel - lo with____ too man - y to wave good - bye.____ oh
time I put all my arms a - round you gonna be some - time next Wednes - day night.____ oh
oc - to - pus and she says to me, "Hon-ey, please buy me 8 dia - mond rings."____ oh

We Are All Earthlings

Words by Sara Compton
Music by Jeff Moss

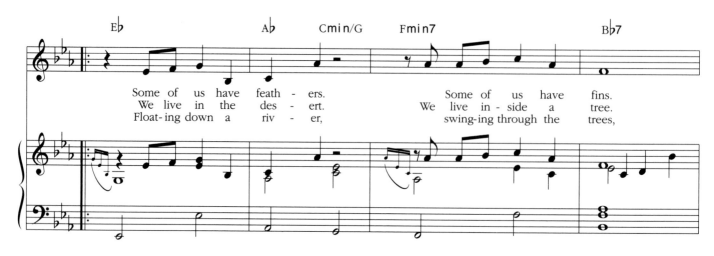

Some of us have feath - ers.   Some of us have fins.
We live in the des - ert.   We live in - side a tree.
Float - ing down a riv - er,   swing - ing through the trees,

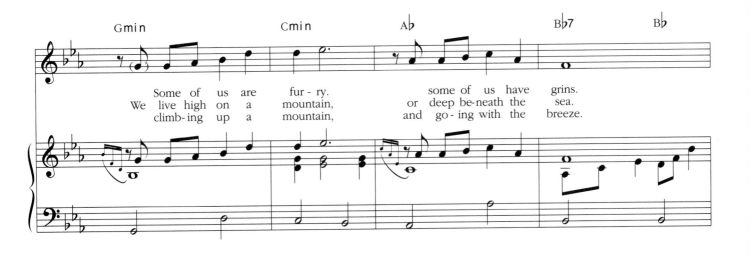

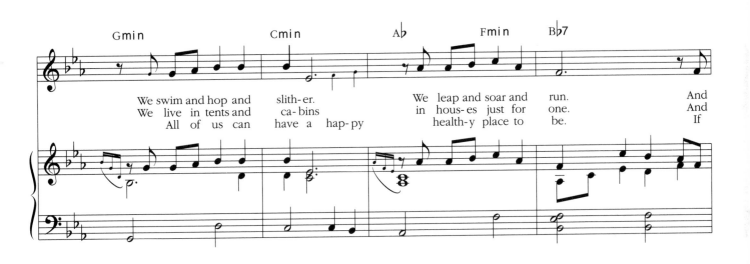

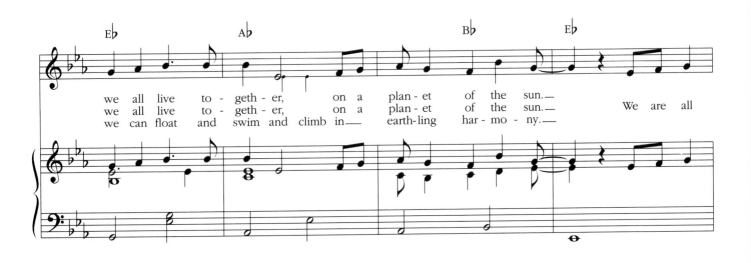

earth - lings.___ We are all earth - lings.___

Spin - ning a - round to - geth - er, on a plan - et___ of the sun.

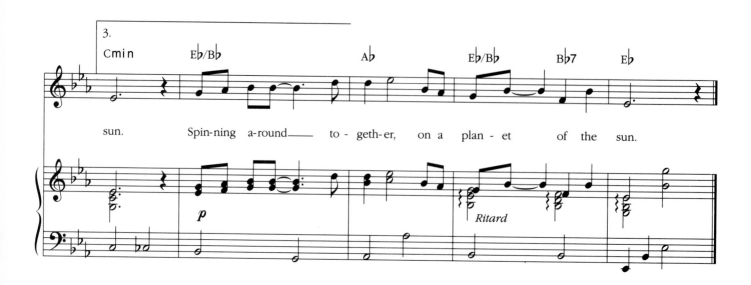

sun. Spin-ning a-round___ to - geth-er, on a plan - et of the sun.

Somebody Come and Play

Words and music by Joe Raposo

Gently

Some - bod - y come and play. ___
Some - bod - y come and play. ___

Some - bod - y come and play to - day. ___ Some - bod - y come and
Some - bod - y come and play my way. ___ Some - bod - y come and

smile the smiles, ___ and sing the songs, it won't take long.
rhyme the rhymes, ___ and laugh the laughs, it won't take time.

Put Down the Duckie

Words by Norman Stiles
Music by Christopher Cerf

Rock Boogie

Ex-
(I)

cuse me Mis - ter Hoots I hate to bug a bus - y bird but I

learned a thing or two I from years of play - in' in a band it's

wan - na learn the sax and I need a help - ful word 'cause I

hard to play a sax - o - phone with some - thing in your hand to

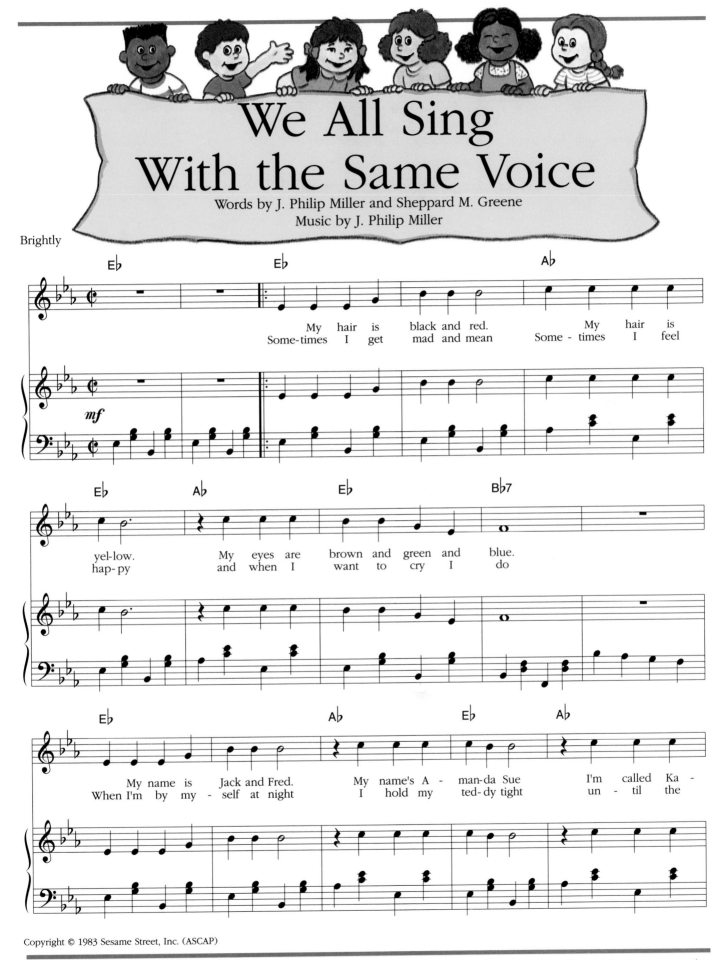

We All Sing With the Same Voice

Words by J. Philip Miller and Sheppard M. Greene
Music by J. Philip Miller

Brightly

My hair is black and red. My hair is
Some-times I get mad and mean Some - times I feel

yel-low. My eyes are brown and green and blue.
hap-py and when I want to cry I do

My name is Jack and Fred. My name's A - man-da Sue I'm called Ka -
When I'm by my - self at night I hold my ted- dy tight un - til the

One of These Things

Words by Jon Stone
Music by Joe Raposo

Breakfast Time

Words and music by Jeff Moss

C = Cookie Monster   E = Ernie

All By Myself

Words and music by Jeff Moss

Moderate

G   Amin   F#Maj 6/D   G   Amin7   F#Maj 6/D

G

You should see me tie my shoe ___ hear me add up
See me pour a glass of juice ___ wig-gle my front

two and two ___ things that I can do all by my-
tooth that's loose ___ things that I can do all by my -

Sing After Me

Words by Tony Geiss
Music by Sam Pottle

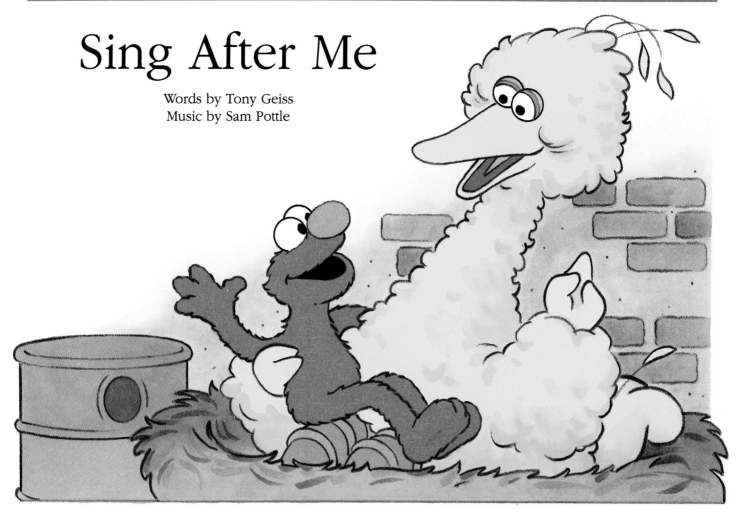

Moderate

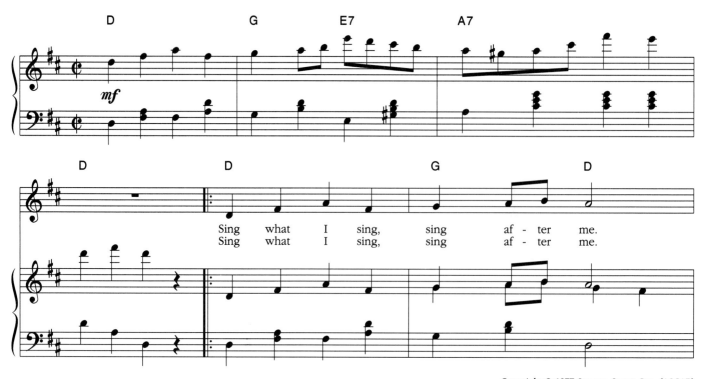

Sing what I sing, sing af-ter me.
Sing what I sing, sing af-ter me.

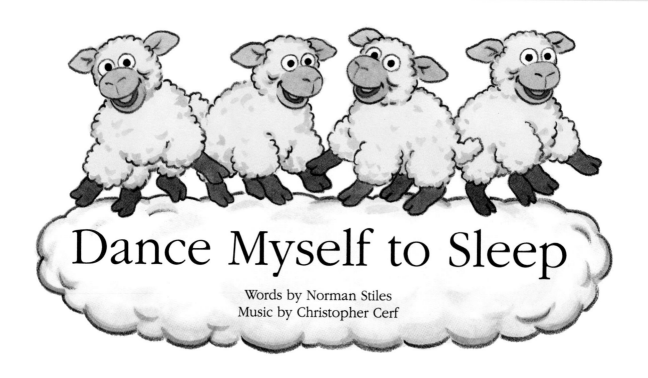

Dance Myself to Sleep

Words by Norman Stiles
Music by Christopher Cerf

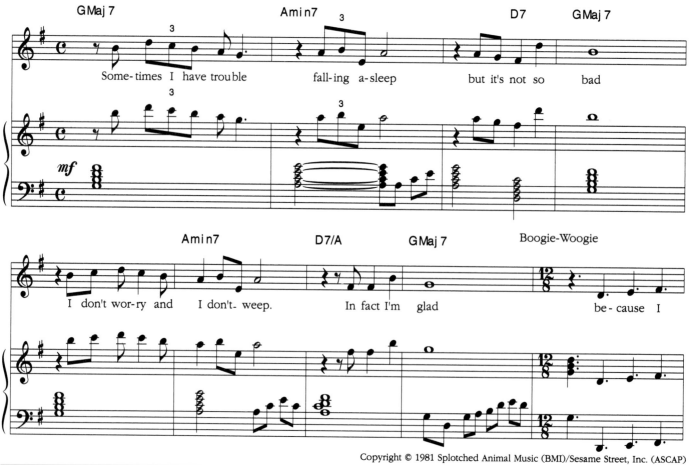

Frogs in the Glen

Words and music by Tony Geiss

Counting is Wonderful

Words by Emily Perl Kingsley and David Axlerod
Music by Sam Pottle

Words and music by Jeff Moss

Happy

Fuzzy and Blue

Words by David Axlerod
Music by Stephen Lawrence

Five People In My Family

Words and music by Jeff Moss

Soft Shoe

Oh I've got

five peo - ple in my fam - 'ly and there's not one of them I'd swap. There is a

Captain Vegetable

Words and music by Jeff Moss

Let's Go Driving

Words and music
by Jeff Moss

Rock

Let's go driv-ing in an au-to-mo-bile___ Let's take a ride in a car___

Lis-ten to the mo-tor go vroom vroom vroom___ as we
Lis-ten to the horn___ go beep beep beep___ as we

trav-el near and far___ vroom vr-vroom___ vr-vroom
trav-el near and far___ beep be-beep___ be-beep

Third Verse:

Let's go driving in an automobile
Let's take a ride in a car.
Windshield wipers go
swish, swish, swish
as we travel near and far.
Swish, sw-swish, sw-swish,
swish, swish, swish
Swish, sw-swish, sw-swish, swish
Swish, sw-swish, sw-swish,
Swish, swish, swish, swish,
Swish, swish, swish, swish, swish.

Fourth Verse:

Let's go driving in an automobile
Let's take a ride in a car.
Listen to the people sing
La, la la
as we travel near and far.
La, la, la, la, la
la, la, la
la, la, la, la, la, la
la, la, la, la, la
la, la, la, la
la, la, la, la, la.

Fifth Verse:

Let's go driving in an automobile
Let's take a ride in a car.
Listen to the sounds we all can hear
as we travel near and far.
vroom, vr-vroom, vr-vroom
vroom, vroom, vroom
beep, be-beep, be-beep, beep
swish, sw-swish, sw-swish,
swish, swish, swish
la, la, la, la, la.

The Batty Bat

Words and music by Joe Raposo

One Fine Face

Words and music by Jeff Moss

What's the Name of that Song?

Words by David Axlerod
Music by Sam Pottle

Brightly

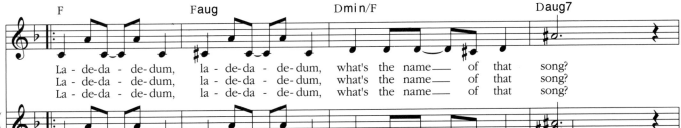

La - de-da - de-dum, la - de-da - de-dum, what's the name___ of that song?
La - de-da - de-dum, la - de-da - de-dum, what's the name___ of that song?
La - de-da - de-dum, la - de-da - de-dum, what's the name___ of that song?

La - de-da - de-dum, la - de-da - de-dum, what's the name___ of that song? It goes
La - de-da - de-dum, la - de-da - de, we mean the name___ of that song? It goes
La - de-da - de-dum, la - de-da - de, they keep on sing - in' that song. They go

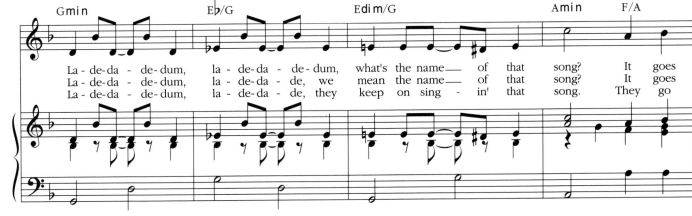

The Grouch Song

Words and music by Jeff Moss

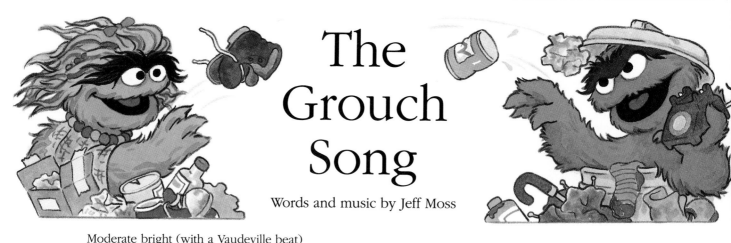

Moderate bright (with a Vaudeville beat)

Lyrics:
If you wake up in the morn-ing mean and grump-y___ and you frown at ev-'ry-bod-y that you see, If you like your oat-meal nice and cold and lump-y,___

Imagine That!

Words and music by Jeff Moss

Moderate

Some-times I im - a - gine that
Some-times I im - a - gine that
Some-times I im - a - gine that

I would like to be a knight in shin-ing ar-mor in a cas-tle by the
I would like to be a dar-ing bold ex-plor-er sail-ing far a-cross the
I would like to be a per-son who's named Ern-ie who looks quite a lot like

sea a knight in shin-ing ar-mor with a prin-cess by my
sea I'd set out on a sail-ing ship to find a dis-tant
me Who likes the things that I like and who does the things I

Opposite Song

Words and music by Christopher Cerf

Moderate Rock

I go— up.— You go down.
(I go— left)— You go right.
(Honey you hang loose) And I'm up-tight.

I go in a straight— line.—
I tra-vel in the day - time.
You know I'm hea-vy ba—by

La La La

Words and music by Joe Raposo

Moderate

La la la la la le - mon.

La la la la la light - bulbs. La la la la

lamp - post. La la la la lump in my oatmeal.

La la la la laugh - ter. La la la la

lul - la-bye.____ La la la la lol-li-pops.

La la la la lights in the sky. La la la la lin -

New Way to Walk

Words by Mark Saltzman
Music by Joe Raposo

Words and music by Christopher Cerf

No park – ing
No camp – ing
No talk – ing

no bik – ing
no cook – ing
no teas – in'

no swim – ming
no laugh – ing
no rhym – in'

Peanut Butter

Moderate

Words and music by Joe Raposo

Takes a lot of lit-tle nuts
(Dump the) pea-nuts from the bag
(Takes a) lot of lit-tle nuts

— to make a jar of pea-nut but-ter 'cause one
— and start 'em on that ol con-vey-or get 'em
— to make a jar of pea-nut but-ter now they're

pea-nut in a jar real-ly does-n't go too
roast-ed and as-sort-ed don't have an-y time to
rea-dy squirt 'em in put the lid on watch 'em

goo taste real - ly good _____ keep it pump - in' through the pipe -
line like a pea - nut but - ter pump - er should _____ takes a
done _____ takes a lot - ta lit - tle nuts and a
lot - ta hard work be - fore the pea - nut but - ter's done _____

D.S. 𝄋 al Coda ⨁

Coda

Muppets Rhyme in School

Words by Sonia Manzano
Music by Joe Raposo

Everyone Makes Mistakes

Words and music by Jeff Moss

I've a spe - cial se - cret chil - dren ought to know; _____
(If you) make a mis - take while count - ing up to ten, _____
(If you) spill a glass of milk all over the floor, _____

Keep the Park
Clean for the Pigeons

Words and music by Tony Geiss

I Heard My Dog Bark

Words and music by Jeff Moss

Lyrics: I was ly-ing in my bed on a qui-et night went down to the kit-chen to get my-self a bite I

Third Verse:

Well the noise was so loud that it hurt my head
It woke up my pet lion who sleeps on my bed
I heard my lion roar (roar!)
I heard my lion roar (roar!)
I heard my horse neigh (neigh!)
I heard my cat meow (meow!)
And standing in the dark I heard my dog bark.

Fourth Verse:

It was the loudest noise that ever there was
It woke up my pet bumblebee and he began to buzz
I heard my bee buzz (buzz!)
I heard my bee buzz (buzz!)
I heard my lion roar (roar!)
I heard my horse neigh (neigh!)
I heard my cat meow (meow!)
And standing in the dark I heard my dog bark.

Fifth Verse:

I put them all to bed all around the house
Soon it was quiet, quiet as a mouse
But then my pet mouse snuck out of his drawer
And he tripped and knocked a big ol' pot on the floor
I heard my dog bark (Woof!)
I heard my dog bark (Woof!)
I heard my dog bark (Woof!)
And standing in the dark I heard my dog bark.

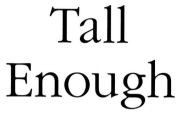

Tall
Enough

Words and music by Jeff Moss

Happy

TALL ENOUGH 143

Reach Your Hand Up High

Words and music by Tony Geiss

Swing

So reach your
(So reach reach your)

hand up high_____ your hand up high_____ and
hand up high_____ your hand up high_____ and

may – be you'll touch the sky_____ reach just a
may – be you'll touch a star_____ reach just a

If Moon Was Cookie

Words by Luis Santeiro
Music by Stephen Lawrence

Proud To Be A

Slowly

Words and music by Tony Geiss

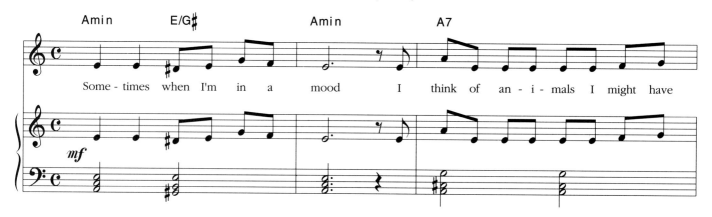

Some - times when I'm in a mood I think of an - i - mals I might have

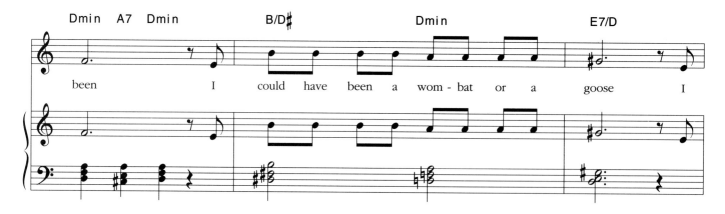

been   I could have been a wom - bat or a goose   I

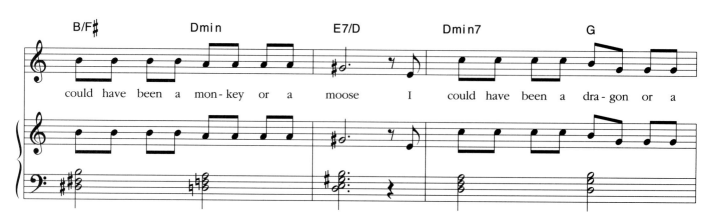

could have been a mon - key or a moose   I could have been a dra - gon or a

x

Ladybugs' Picnic

Words by Don Hadley
Music by William Luckey

Brightly

One two three, four five six, seven eight nine, ten 'leven twelve, la - dy - bugs came,_____ to the la - dy - bugs' pic - nic.

La - dy-bugs twelve_____ at the la - dy-bugs' pic - nic. They
played jump rope but the rope it broke so they just sat a - round tel - lin'
knock knock jokes. La - dy- bugs twelve_____ at the la - dy-bugs' pic - nic.
One two three, four five six,

What Do I Do When I'm Alone?

Words and music by Jeff Moss

I'm Going to Get My Hair Cut

Words and music by Jeff Moss

Moderate

I'm going to get my hair cut
Me going to get me fur cut

I've never done that be-
Me gone plen-ty of times be-

fore _____ I know I once cut my
fore _____ It not like cutting me

Imagination Song

Words and music by Joe Raposo

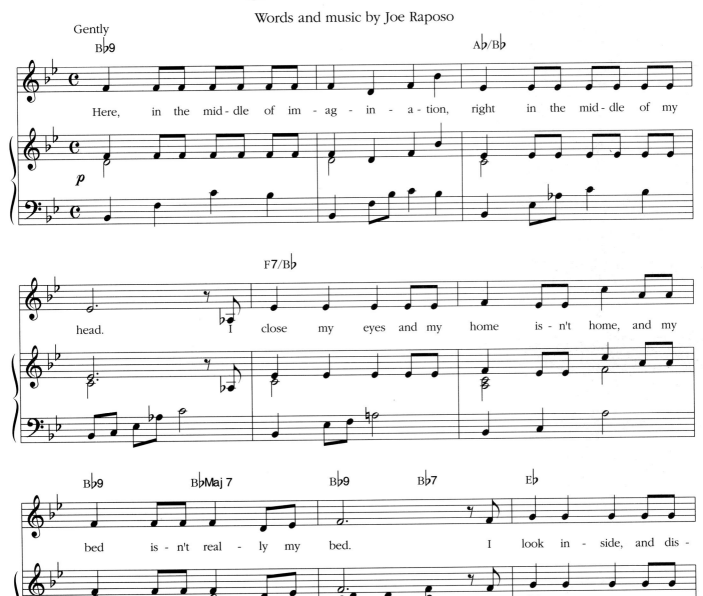

Gently

Here, in the mid-dle of im-ag-in-a-tion, right in the mid-dle of my head. I close my eyes and my home is-n't home, and my bed is-n't real-ly my bed. I look in-side, and dis-

Monster in the Mirror

Words by Norman Stiles
Music by Christopher Cerf

Born to Add

Words and music by
Christopher Cerf

Bright Rock

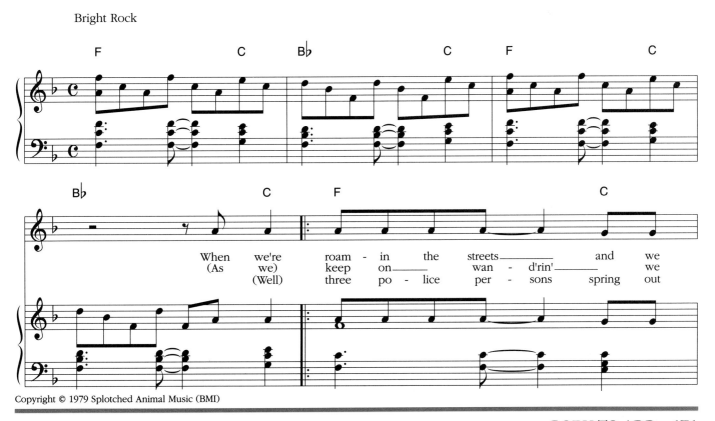

When we're roam - in the streets_____ and we
(As we) keep on_____ wan - d'rin'_____ we
(Well) three po - lice per - sons spring out

It Sure Is Hot!

Words by Sarah Durkee
Music by Paul Jacobs

Latin

A girl named Ro-sa-li-ta moved in down the block
(The boy from) up the block just to-tal-ly made my day

I real-ly like her but I'm much too shy to talk To have a
but I'm too shy to think of an-y-thing to say To have a

On My Pond

Words by Sarah Durkee
Music by Christopher Cerf

Moderate

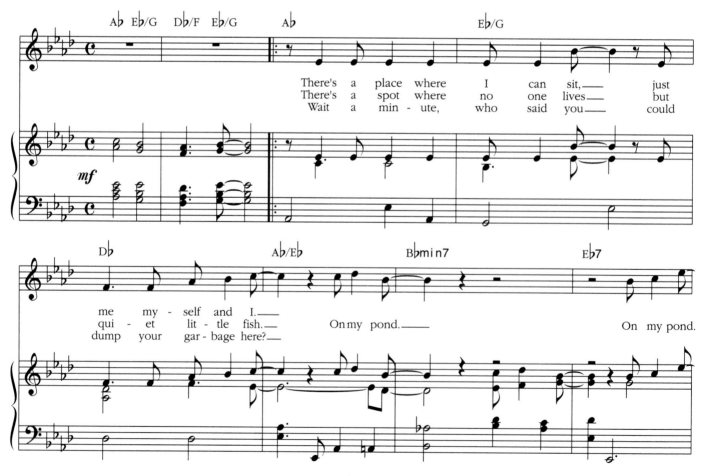

There's a place where I can sit,— just
There's a spot where no one lives— but
Wait a min-ute, who said you— could

me my-self and I.— On my pond.— On my pond.
qui-et lit-tle fish.— On my pond.—
dump your gar-bage here?—

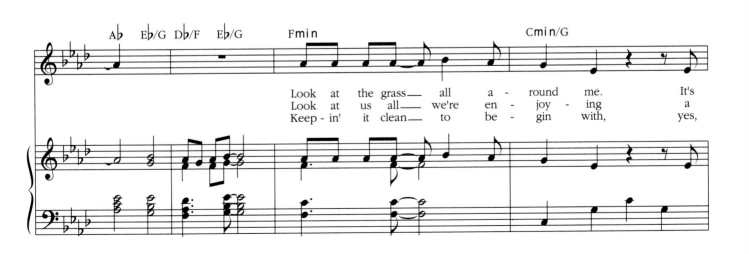

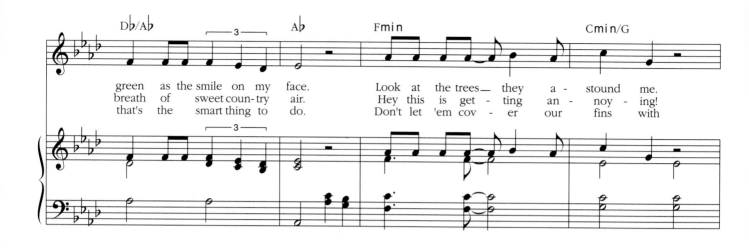

green as the smile on my face.
breath of sweet coun-try air.
that's the smart thing to do.

Look at the trees— they a - stound me.
Hey this is get - ting an - noy - ing!
Don't let 'em cov - er our fins with

Wow what a beau - ti - ful place!
Please keep it down o - ver there.
an - y more black slim - y goo!

Save a place where

I can sit, just me, my - self, and I.— On my pond.—

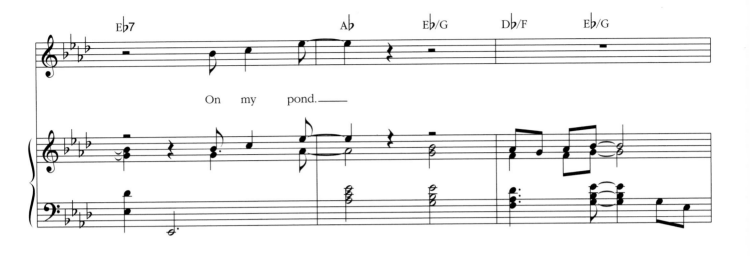

On my pond.——

Keep the wa - ter fresh and clean and peace - ful as a sigh.

On my pond.—— On my pond.

One Small Voice

Words and music by Jeff Moss

Ev - 'ry song the world sings, each was once un - known.
No tune is too sim - ple. No voice can be wrong.

Some - bo - dy felt a song in - side and was - n't a - fraid to
Mu - sic can come from an - y heart and an - y - one's voice can

A Little Bit

Words and music by Joe Raposo

If I Were

Words by David Axlerod
Music by Stephen Lawrence

If I were a po - et I would write a son - net
Did you guess my se - cret? I am not a po - et

it would say, "I love you." Your name would be on it.
could - n't write a son - net and I think you know it.

Doin' the Pigeon

Words and music by Joe Raposo

Moderate

Ev'-ry-time I feel a-lone and slight-ly blue,

that's when I be-gin to think that's what I'd like to start to do.

And though it may not be the kind of thing that's quite your cup of

Pat Pat Patty Pat

Words by Jerry Juhl
Music by Joe Raposo

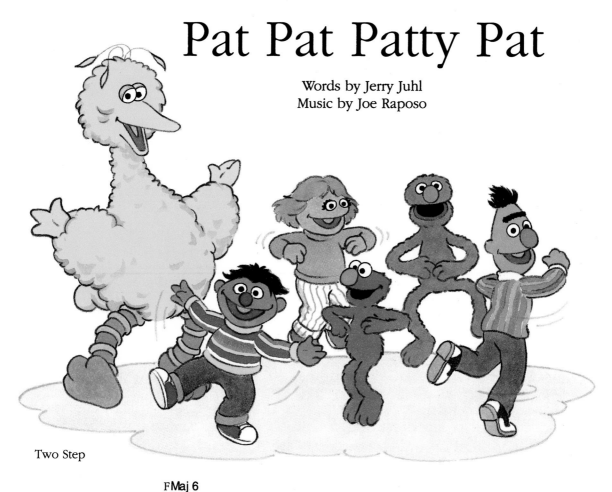

Two Step

Oh, lis-ten to the song that's hum-ming in your ear and you'll have more fun than you've had all year. Just shake your leg with a

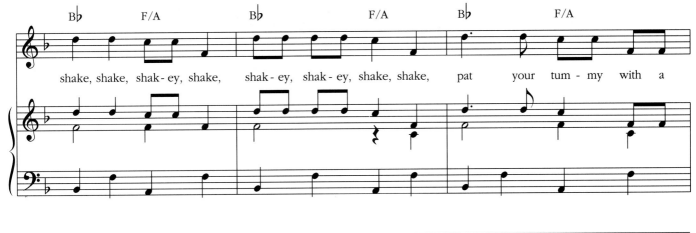

shake, shake, shak-ey, shake, shak-ey, shak-ey, shake, shake, pat your tum-my with a

pat, pat, pat-ty, pat, pat-ty, pat-ty, pat, pat-poo! Oh, poo!

Second verse:

Oh, listen to the song that's humming in your ear and you'll have more fun than you've had all year.

Just wiggle your fingers with a wiggle, wiggle, wiggle, wiggle, wiggle, wiggle, wiggle, wiggle Shake your legs...
Pat your tummy...

Third verse:

Oh, listen to the song that's humming in your ear and you'll have more fun than you've had all year.

Just flap your arms with a flap, flap, flappy flap flappy, flappy, flap, flap Wiggle your fingers...
Shake your legs...
Pat your tummy...

Fourth verse:

Oh, listen to the song that's humming in your ear and you'll have more fun than you've had all year.

Just spin around with a spin, spin, spinny spin, spinny, spinny, spin, spin Flap your arms...
Wiggle your fingers...
Shake your legs...
Pat your tummy...

Fifth verse:

Oh, listen to the song that's humming in your ear and you'll have more fun than you've had all year.

Just hop around with a hop, hop, hoppy hop, hoppy hoppy, hop, hop Spin around...
Flap your arms...
Wiggle your fingers...
Shake your legs...
Pat your tummy...

Caribbean Amphibian

Words and music by Mark Saltzman

Honker Duckie Dinger Jamboree

Words by Norman Stiles
Music by Christopher Cerf

Moderate

Come on ev-'ry-bo-dy to a
Take a chance and join us and I
Want to be a mem-ber of our

street called Ses-a-me there's some-thing ve-ry sil-ly that we'd
know that you'll a-gree our show may not be fan-cy but it's
hap-py fam-i-ly no-thing to it you can do it if you

When Bert's Not Here

Words and music by Joe Raposo

Light & Easy

When
(When)

Bert's not here the hours last for-ev-er the toys aren't fun and the
Bert's not here the place is too qui-et the win-dows creak fun-ny

cook - ies don't crunch.___ When Bert's not here I don't feel so clev-er and I
thoughts fill my head.___ When Bert's not here no way to de-ny it I

Eight Beautiful Notes

Words and music by Jeff Moss

Freely

I play eight notes they sound like this.
(I) play the eight notes go - ing down.

When I play them I can't miss.
I play eight notes all o - ver town.

First I play them one by one.
First I play them one by one.

Keep Christmas With You

Words by David Axlerod
Music by Sam Pottle

When Christ - mas time is ov - er and pres - ents put a - way, don't be

sad, there'll be so much to trea - sure a -

bout this Christ - mas day and the fun we've

True Blue Miracle

Happy

Words and music by Carol Hall

have to let them show.___ May - be that's___ why ev - 'ry - one___ be -

gins to get a glow___ and fill their hearts with Christ - mas

spi - rit they can share;___ that's the best part of Christ - mas.

and if that is - n't a true___ blue mir - a - cle I don't know what one is.

Index of First Lines

Index of Song Titles